Where Is Pete?
¿Dónde está Pedrito?

by Deborah Schecter

ISBN: 978-1-338-70283-5
Illustrated by Anne Kennedy
Copyright © 2020 by Deborah Schecter. All rights reserved.
Published by Scholastic Inc., 557 Broadway, New York, NY 10012

10 9 8 7 6   68   23 24 25 26/0

Printed in Jiaxing, China. First printing, June 2020.

■■SCHOLASTIC

Where is Petey?
Is he under the bed?

¿Dónde está Pedrito?
¿Está debajo de la cama?

Is he in the shed?

¿Está en el cobertizo?

Is he behind the door?

¿Está detrás de la puerta?

Is he in the drawer?

¿Está en el cajón?

Is he in the tub?

¿Está en la bañera?

Is he under the rug?

¿Está debajo de la alfombra?

Here is Petey!

¡Aquí está Pedrito!